Compare Bears® Maths

Book 1

Barbara Hewett

The Author

With over twenty years experience of infant teaching, Barbara
Hewett has lectured on teaching infant maths and ran a maths
centre for teachers. She now devotes her time to writing and has
many publications including contribution to a major primary
maths scheme.

Photocopying

Compare Bears may be ordered direct from LDA.
00943

Compare Bears Maths Book 1

00613
ISBN 1 85503 105 1

© Illustration Susan Perkins
© Text Barbara Hewett

COMPARE BEARS® is a registered trade mark.
Design of COMPARE BEARS © Learning Resources, Inc.

Reprinted 1994, 1995, 1996

LDA, Duke Street, Wisbech, Cambs PE13 2AE, England

Introduction

The Compare Bears families offer an ideal way to get young children thinking and talking about early mathematical concepts. In three sizes, three weights and four colours, the bears can help with counting, matching, sorting and weighing.

This book is designed for use in conjunction with the Compare Bears. The activities an games are aimed at developing basic mathematical understanding, skills and vocabulary.

The topics are structured so that the children work in groups for each set of activities and then work individually through the appropriate activity sheets. They may like to record each activity sheet they complete on the individual record sheet. The page facing the record sheet can also be copied, coloured and stuck on as a front cover for a personal folder for work with the bears.

The teacher's notes for each activity include:

● the aim of the activity
● the vocabulary to be used
● any materials additional to the bears that is required
● extra activities for follow-up work
● instructions for the activity sheets and games.

The topics may be used in any order; they could for example be used as an introduction to a new topic in an existing mathematics scheme where practical work and special vocabulary is required. They do, however, follow an organised progression through sorting, matching, counting, patterns, weight, area, height, odd and even numbers, grids, money and probability. Starting with numbers 1 to 5, there is then a slow progression up to 10 as some children need more practice than others in order to understand and memorise numbers 0 and 6 to 10.

The activities should preceed the activity sheets. They are the key to progress. Only through the activities can children learn to use the vocabulary essential to mathematical understanding.

The wording on the activity sheets is very simple. Even so, some children may need help to read the instructions. Children should not be prevented from attempting the activity sheets because of inability to read.

Bears are represented by either pictures of bears in three sizes or, on some sheets, by stools in three sizes. Children do not have to draw the bears but can choose from cut-out pictures in three sizes. A photocopy master for these can be found on page 93. These can be copied, cut up and kept in a box for the children to use.

Similarly, pages 89-92 are photocopy masters for the various labels needed for some activities. These may be copied, mounted on card and covered with transparent plastic. The activity sheets with games on may also be coloured and covered.

In this second edition of Compare Bears Maths Book 1 the words 'mummy', 'daddy', and 'baby' have been replaced with 'medium', 'large' and 'small'.

Compare Bears Maths Book 1 is compatible with any mathematics scheme and the material matches major schemes at the following levels:

Heinemann	Mathematics 1 and 2
Ginn	National Curriculum Mathematics Level 1, Reception
Longman	Nuffield Maths Level 1
Cambridge University Press	Cambridge Primary Mathematics, Module 1
Nelson	Nelson Mathematics, Towards Level 1 Maths Chest, 1 and 2 New Peak, Key Stage 1, Level 1
Collins	Steps, Level 1

Contents

Front cover   vi

Record Sheet   vii

Name the colours   *sorting by colour*   1
Activity Sheet 1   2

Name the sizes   *sorting by size*   3
Activity Sheet 2   4

Three bears   *matching the sizes*   5
Activity Sheet 3   6

Match and compare sets   *one-to-one matching*   7
Activity Sheet 4   8

More, fewer, the same   *matching and comparing numbers*   9
Activity Sheet 5   10

Counting to 5   *counting and ordering to 5*   11
Activity Sheet 6   12

Counting to 6   *recognising sets 0 to 6*   13
Activity Sheet 7   14

All in order   *putting the bears in order*   15
Activity Sheet 8   16

Changing patterns   *copying and repeating patterns*   17
Activity Sheet 9   18

Small, larger, largest   *sorting, matching, ordering and comparing*   19
Activity Sheet 10   20

Matching bears on grids   *sorting and matching on to grids*   21
Activity Sheet 11   22
Activity Sheet 12   23
Activity Sheet 13   24

Sorting with one or two attributes   25
Activity Sheet 14   26
Activity Sheet 15   27
Activity Sheet 16   *a Venn diagram*   28
Activity Sheet 17   *a Carroll diagram*   29
Activity Sheet 18   *a sorting tree*   30

Continue the pattern   *continuing patterns in size and colour*   31
Activity Sheet 19   32

Bears on the balance   *practice in weighing*   33
Activity Sheet 20   34

Light, heavier, heaviest   *comparing weight of individual bears*   35
Activity Sheet 21   36

Weighs more than, weighs less than   *comparing combined weight of bears*   37
Activity Sheet 22   38
Activity Sheet 23   39
Activity Sheet 24   40

Weigh several bears   *weighing several bears together*   41
Activity Sheet 25   42

Add, group and subtract the bears   *adding two sets of bears*   43
Activity Sheet 26   44
Activity Sheet 27   45
Activity Sheet 28   46

Numbers up to 10   *counting and ordering*   47
Activity Sheet 29   48
Activity Sheet 30   49
Activity Sheet 31   50
Activity Sheet 32   51

Activity Sheet 33		52
Activity Sheet 34		53
Activity Sheet 35		54
Activity Sheet 36		55
Activity Sheet 37	*join the dots*	56
Sorting on to the grid and changing the colour	*sorting and changing attributes*	57
Activity Sheet 38		58
Activity Sheet 39		59
Activity Sheet 40		60
Picnic cloths	*choosing appropriate attributes for sorting*	61
Activity Sheet 41		62
A handful of bears	*measuring area*	63
Activity Sheet 42		64
Short, taller, tallest	*comparing height*	65
Activity Sheet 43		66
Activity Sheet 44		67
Activity Sheet 45		68
Activity Sheet 46		69
Activity Sheet 47		70
Odd and even numbers	*introducing odd and even numbers*	71
Activity Sheet 48		72
Activity Sheet 49		73
Activity Sheet 50	*Odds and evens game*	74
Counting in 2s	*counting in 2s*	75
Activity Sheet 51		76

More addition	*addition to 10, rows and columns*	77
Activity Sheet 52	*the addition square*	78
Activity Sheet 53	*addition to 10*	79
Activity Sheet 54	*round and round the garden game*	80
Activity Sheet 55	*four in a line game*	81
Activity Sheet 56	*circles game*	82
Paying with pennies	*using penny coins*	83
Activity Sheet 57		84
Activity Sheet 58		85
Activity Sheet 59		86
Probability	*discovering how chance works*	87
Activity Sheet 60		88
Labels for activities		89
Bear pictures for cut-outs		93

COMPARE BEARS WORK

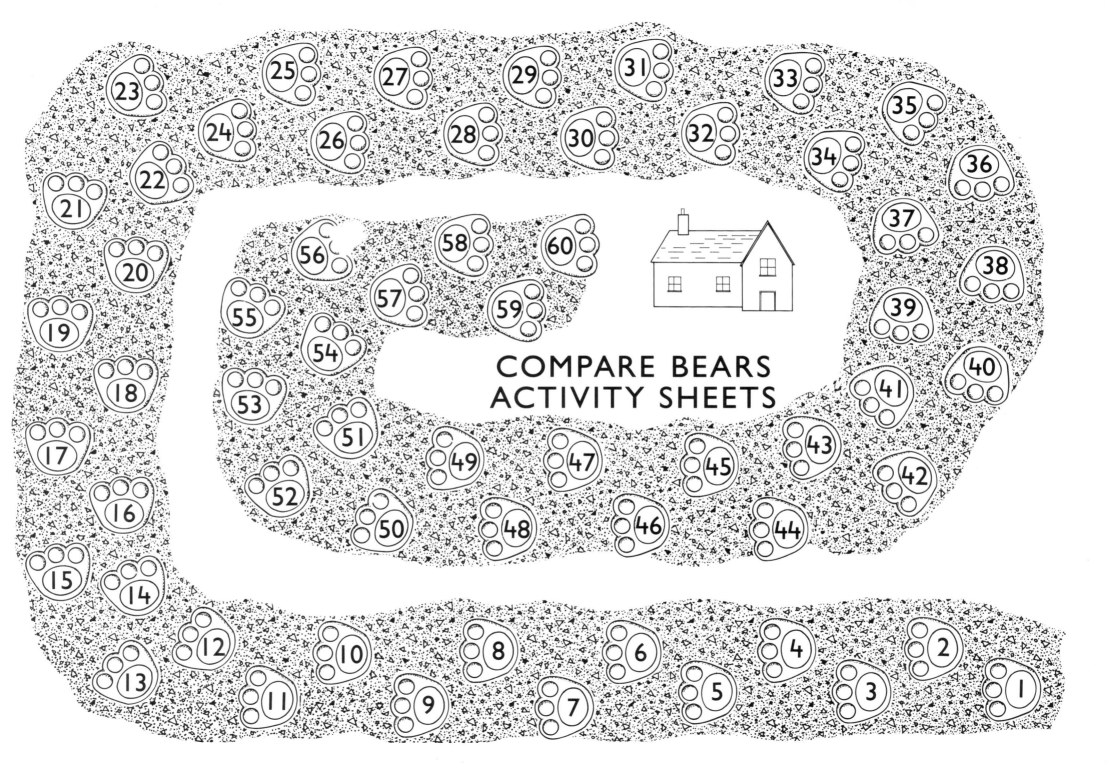

COMPARE BEARS
ACTIVITY SHEETS

Name the colours

Aim

To classify the bears by colour
To name and sort the colours

Vocabulary

Colour, red, blue, green, yellow, sort, match, same, different, set, plastic

Materials

Colour cards for red, blue, green and yellow
Four hoops or four sheets of paper

Activity 1   Free play

This activity simply gives the children an opportunity to play freely with the Compare Bears before introducing them to a more structured mathematical approach.
Encourage the children to talk about the colours, shapes, sizes and feel of the bears.
Encourage them to make up their own stories about the bears.

Activity 2   Find the colour

Hold up a bear. Ask a child to name the colour then pick up another bear the same colour. Find the right colour card and place it beside the bears.

The same child can then pick up a bear of another colour and ask a different child to name the colour and find a bear to match. Find the right colour card and place it beside the bears. Repeat for the other two colours.

Activity 3   Sorting by colour

Set out the hoops, or papers and ask a child to label them with the colour cards. Ask 'What colour bears will go in the hoops?' Let the children sort the bears and talk about the results. Say, 'Tell me about the bears in this hoop. What about their colour and size? How are the bears alike? How are they different? Name some other things of the same colour.'

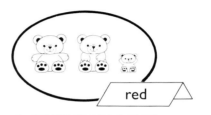 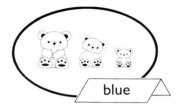

ACTIVITY SHEET 1

Materials

Coloured pencils

Children should clearly understand the use of the arrow to record the relationship between the bears. Here the arrow says 'is the same colour'
Help the children to read the names of the colours.

Extra activities

Ask the children to bring their own teddy bears to school.
Let them talk about their bears and introduce them to the group.
Sort the bears in the same way as Activity 1.
Encourage the children to think of other ways of sorting, for example by texture.
Different relationships, other than colour, can be recorded in several ways by the children.

Colour and join

is the same colour

$\longleftrightarrow$

yellow

blue

red

red

green

red

blue

green

red

yellow

Name the sizes

Aim

To classify the bears according to their size

Vocabulary

Large, small, medium, sort, same, different, match, red, yellow, blue, green, set, family, group

Materials

Cards for large, small, medium
Three hoops or three sheets of paper, a bag

Activity 1   Find the size

Hold up a large blue, medium blue and small blue bear.
Compare and name the different sizes. Place the right size card beside each bear. Hold up a bear and ask a child to say the size and find another bear the same size. The same child then picks up a bear and asks another child to name the size, find a bear to match, then place the right card beside the bears.
Repeat with other sizes.

Activity 2   In the bag

Put some bears of various sizes into a bag.
Ask a child to feel for a large bear and then pass the bag on, saying the size to be found by the next child.

Activity 3   Sorting by size

Lay out the hoops or sheets of paper and ask a child to label them with the size cards. Ask 'What size bears will go in the hoops?'
Let the children sort the bears and then ask them to talk about the sets they have made. Say 'Tell me about the bears in this set. How are they alike? How are they different?'

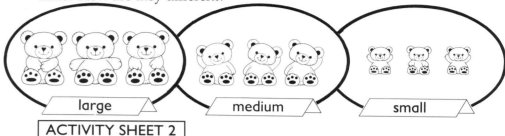

large   medium   small

ACTIVITY SHEET 2

Materials

Cut-out pictures of bears in three sizes (from p. 93), coloured pencils, glue

The children sort the bears into families of 3 on to the activity sheet. Help them to identify the three sizes of pictures before they are stuck into the sets. Finally the children can colour and label the families.

Extra activities

Continue the family theme using children's own teddy bears. Talk about the type of home the children and their bears live in. Display illustrations of a house, flat, bungalow, terrace house and so on and ask the children to draw a picture of their bear. Using an arrow which represents the relationship 'lives in a', the children draw a line from their bear to their house.
Ask the children to make their own diagrams of the people in their families with their bear in the centre. The children draw all the people with whom they live and link the bear to them with an arrow that says 'lives with'.

Liam's bear   lives in a   house
Emma's bear   caravan

Find three different size bears for each family. Label the family red, blue, yellow or green.

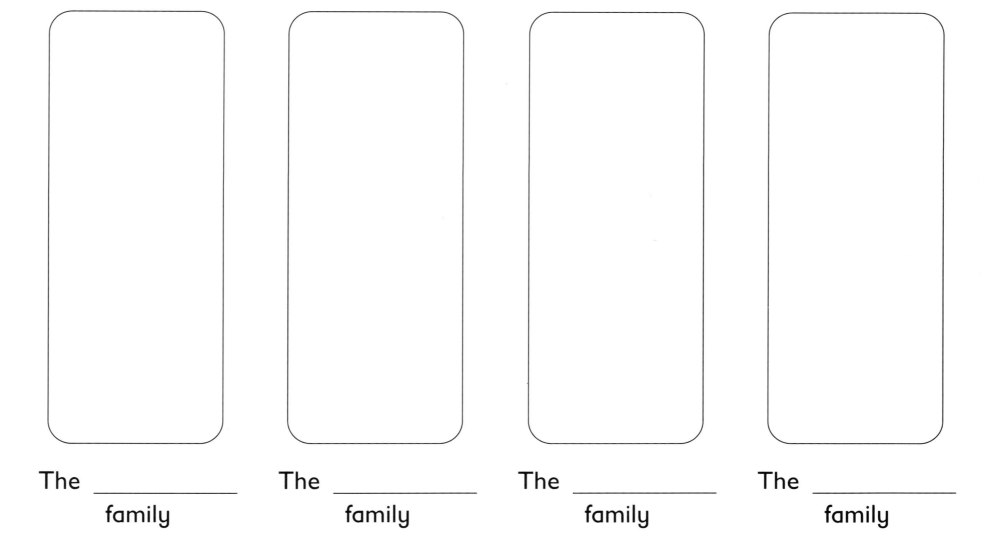

The _____
family

The _____
family

The _____
family

The _____
family

Three bears

Aim

To match according to size

Vocabulary

Belongs to, same, different

Materials

Plasticine or Playdoh, boards for plasticine

Put out a family of 3 bears: a large, a medium and a small bear.
Remind the children of the story of Goldilocks. Ask the children to choose
their own family of bears. Each child has a board and uses the plasticine to
make a bed, a bowl and a chair to fit one of the bears.
Display the boards and bears with arrows.

belongs to

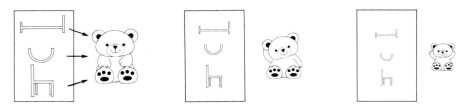

ACTIVITY SHEET 3

Materials

Coloured pencils

Children match and colour the line of bears and decide, irrespective of
colour, which bear is the same size as the bear in the margin.
Talk about the differences between the bears. Encourage the children to
talk about the bears which are larger and smaller and also about the ones
which are too large or too small to match the one in the margin.

Extra activities

Children can use their own teddy bears to compare three bears at a time to
find the large, medium and small bear. They can also find bears which are
the same size.

Find children in the class who are the same height.
Explore the classroom for objects to compare in the same way.

Kim's game
Make a line of four different coloured and different sized Compare Bears.

Tell the children to look at them carefully. While the children close their
eyes, mix up the bears and remove one bear. The first child to identify the
missing bear is the winner and will be the one to select and remove the
bear in the next game. Gradually increase the number of bears in the line.
The children can also play Kim's game with their own teddy bears.

Match the line of bears. Colour the bears which are the same size.

Match and compare sets

Aim

To practise one-to-one matching

Vocabulary

Match, same number, different, more, less, fewer, set, between

Activity 1   One-to-one

Put out five large, five medium and five small bears. Ask the children to match one medium bear to one large bear. Ask 'Is there the same number of medium bears as large bears? Now match one small bear to each medium bear. Are there the same number of small bears as medium bears? The same number of small bears as large bears?'
Line up the large, medium and small bears and check.

ACTIVITY SHEET 4
Materials

Coloured pencils

Point out to the children that the stools in the sets are in three sizes. Children match the bears to the stools so they can sit in the sets. By matching the bears and by drawing lines between the two sets they can see which set has more.

Sit the bears on their stools. Match the sets. Colour the set with more bears.

 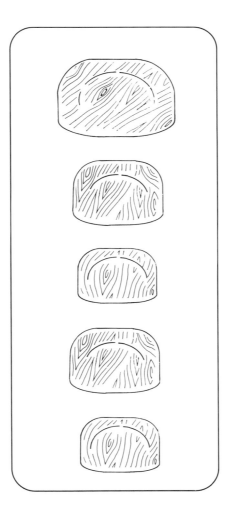 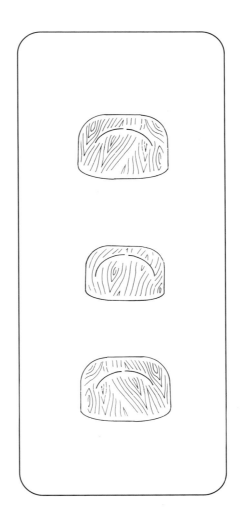 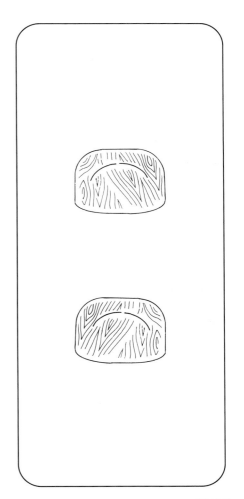

More, fewer, the same

Aim

To match and compare sets to find which set has more or fewer members

Vocabulary

Match sets, compare, same, different, more, fewer, less, number, larger, smaller, group

Activity 1   More bears

Put out five small bears and four bricks. Ask a child to give each bear a brick. Encourage the child to talk about matching the bears and bricks by the 'one for you and one for you' method. Ask 'Is there the same number of bricks as bears? Are there more bears / fewer bears / is there a different number of bears?'

Activity 2   Fewer large bears

Put out five large bears and six medium bears. Ask a child to match the large bears with the medium bears. Encourage the child to talk about the method of matching – one large bear with one medium bear. Repeat the questions about the same number, more, fewer and a different number of bears.

Activity 3   The same, more and fewer

Put out five medium bears in a group. Ask a child to make a larger group of large bears. Ask 'Which group has more bears? Which has fewer bears?' Ask another child to take the medium bears and make a smaller group of small bears. Ask 'Are there fewer or more small bears than medium bears?' Line up the three groups. Match the bears and compare the difference between the groups. Ask, 'Which is a larger group? Which is a smaller group? How can you make the groups the same?'

ACTIVITY SHEET 5

Materials

Coloured pencils

Remind the children that the stools are in different sizes and are for the bears to sit on. Children find the word 'fewer' difficult to use and understand. Mathematically, 'fewer' is used with single objects such as bricks and bears. 'Less' is used with continuous materials such as sand and water. Talk about matching the bears by drawing lines up to the set *above* or *down* to the set *below*. Children can also make *pairs* of the bears until one set is empty so they can see which set has fewer bears.

Sit the bears on their stools. Match the sets.

Colour the set with fewer bears.

Colour the set with fewer bears.

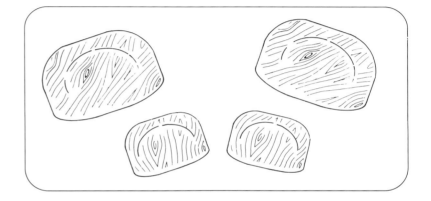

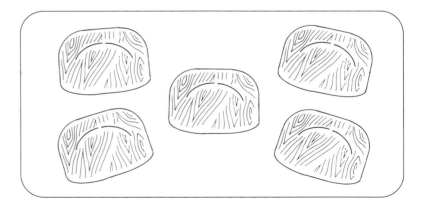

Counting to 5

Aim

To practise counting and ordering to 5

Vocabulary

One, two, three, four, five, none, zero, count, order, match, correct, forwards, backwards

Materials

Number cards: 0, 1, 2, 3, 4, 5

| 0 | 1 | 2 | 3 | 4 | 5 |

Activity 1   Count to 5

Ask each child to take five bears from the set and line them up. Encourage them to place a finger on each bear as they count – 1, 2, 3, 4, 5. Rearrange the bears and count again. Ask them to look at the numbers, put them in order and place a finger on each number as they count. Ask them to try counting backwards.

Activity 2   And one more

Put out six pots or box lids and number cards 0 to 5. Ask the children to place the cards in order on the lids and then to place the correct number of bears in the lids. Take the bears out of the lids and match them up in lines.

Say, 'Here is one bear. One more bear makes two bears, and one more makes ... and one more ... and one more.'

Activity 3   Number by colour

Put out large bears: one red, two blue, three green and four yellow, and number cards 0 to 4. Ask the children to sort the bears and place them in groups beside the cards in the correct order.

Activity 4   Number by size

Put out   five small red bears   four medium blue bears
            three large green bears   two small yellow bears
            one medium red bear   number cards 0 to 5.

Ask the children to sort the bears and place them beside the cards in the correct order.

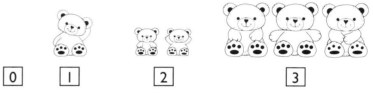

Next, the children can work in pairs. They each make up groups of bears by size or colour to match the numbers 0 to 5. They mix up the bears before handing them over to their partner to sort.

ACTIVITY SHEET 6

Materials

Coloured pencils

Remind the children that the stools are in three sizes to fit the bears. Ask them to point to each number and say the name before they place the bears in the sets. Colour the stools to match the sets.

The children can then write the numbers in the same way on another sheet and rearrange the bears to make up their own sets to match the numbers.

Match the bears to the stools. Draw lines to the numbers.

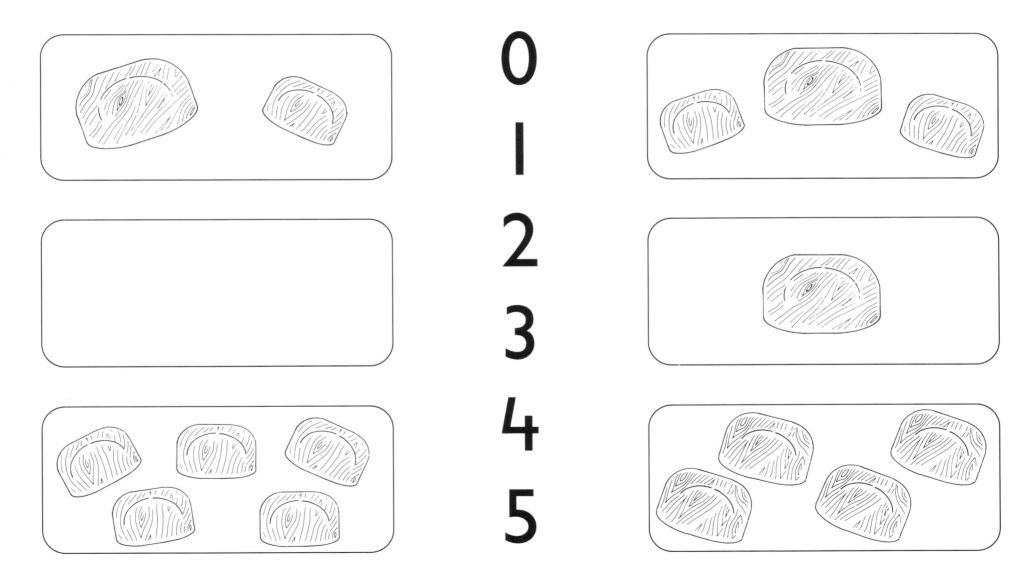

0
1
2
3
4
5

© LDA Compare Bears Maths Book 1

Counting to 6

Aim

To recognise sets 0 to 6

Vocabulary

Zero, one, two, three, four, five, six, number, correct

Materials

Number cards: 0, 1, 2, 3, 4, 5, 6

seven size cards

seven counters in red, blue, green and yellow

Activity 1   Six bears

Place the number cards 0 to 6 face down on the table. Ask each child to take a card, read the number and then choose that number of bears. They can choose bears of any colour and size. Put the bears with matching cards in order. Count and check the number of bears.
Ask:
   'Which is the first number ... the last number?'
   'Which is the smallest number ... the largest number?'
   'Which is one more than 1, 2, 3, 4, 5?'
   'Which number comes between 1 and 3, 2 and 4, 3 and 5?'
   'Which number comes before/after 2, 3, 4, 5, 6?'
Shuffle the cards and repeat the activity.

Activity 2   Six bears by colour

Repeat Activity 1, but this time put out seven counters in the colours red, blue, green and yellow. Children choose a counter with the card and have to collect the correct number and colour of bears to match the card and counter. They can choose bears of any size.

Activity 3   Five bears by colour and size

Repeat Activity 2, this time adding the seven size cards placed face down, which show a large bear, or a medium bear or a small bear. Remove the number card 6. Now the children will have to choose the correct number of bears by colour and size.

Activity 4   Two sets together

Line up the set of three bears. Ask 'Which two sets together will match these bears?' Match sets 1 and 2 and place the cards beside them .

Tell them 'One and two bears together make three bears. Together they make the same number.'
Repeat with: 4 bears and sets 1 and 3
   5 bears and sets 2 and 3
   6 bears and sets 1 and 5, 2 and 4.

ACTIVITY SHEET 7

Materials

Coloured pencils

Ask the children to read the number words before they start to assemble the bears in the sets. They can mix colours and sizes in the sets.
On the back of the sheet, the children can write the numbers and different words and rearrange the bears to show six different assemblies of bears.

Copy the number. Write the word. Make the sets of bears. Draw and colour the stools.

1 one	2 two	3 three	4 four	5 five	6 six

All in order

Aim

To practise putting the bears in order

Vocabulary

First, second, third, fourth, fifth, sixth, last, behind, in front, next to, beside, on either side, queue

Materials

Coloured pencils, cotton reels for pretend bus stops

Activity 1   Where in the queue

Line up six bears of varied size and colour. Ask the children to say the colour and name of each bear, for example 'a large green bear'.
Turn the bears to face the bus-stop.
Ask 'Who is the first / last in the queue? Who is second .... sixth?'
Continue the questions using the words listed in the vocabulary. Repeat them several times.
Ask the children to make their own lines of bears and to question each other about the position of the bears.

Activity 2   Make a queue

Ask each child to put a small yellow bear on the table to face the bus-stop. Encourage them to listen carefully.
Give instructions:
  'Put a medium yellow bear behind the small yellow bear.'
  'Put a small blue bear next to the small yellow bear.'
  'Put a large blue bear in front of the small blue bear.'
  'Put a medium green bear first in the queue and a large red bear last.'
  'How many bears in the queue?'

Rearrange the queue of bears. Ask the children to describe the queue: 'My first bear is ... My second bear is ...'

Activity 3   Change the size

Put out a mixed line of three large bears and three medium bears. Ask a child to copy the line of bears, but to change the large bears for medium bears and the medium bears for small bears.

Repeat the activity with other sizes and sequences. Let the children make up lines of two different sizes. They must decide on the changes to be made: large for medium, small for medium, etc.

ACTIVITY SHEET 8

Materials

Cut-outs of all three sizes of bears (use bears on p. 93), glue

Let the children assemble a line of bears corresponding to the top line of bears on the activity sheet. Help them to read the change instructions. Use bears for the change and then put the cut-outs in place.

Change small bears for medium bears and large bears for small bears.

Changing patterns

Aim

To practise copying and repeating patterns

Vocabulary

First, second, third, fourth, fifth, sixth, next, after, beside, on either side, behind, before, between, begin, large, medium, small

Activity 1   Repeat patterns in colour

Put out three small green bears and three small red bears.
Alternate the colours: g r g r g r.
Ask the children to describe the pattern and positions of the bears.
Explain and demonstrate the use of the words listed in the vocabulary.
Tell the children they may change the colours of the pattern. They must say what changes they are going to make, for example:
  Change one colour only: green for blue.
  Change both colours: green for blue, red for yellow.
  Reverse the colours.

Activity 2   Repeat patterns in size

Put out three medium bears and three large bears.
Alternate the sizes: l m l m l m.
Repeat Activity 1. This time substitute the bears changing the size.

Activity 3   Repeat patterns in colour and size

Put out three large red bears and three small blue bears

Repeat Activity 1. Encourage the children to describe the colour, size and position of each bear. Help them to decide on the changes they will make. This time try changing the colour and the size.
Reverse the size but keep the same colour
Reverse the colour but keep the same size.
Change large for medium or small.
Change small for medium or large.
Change one or both colours.

ACTIVITY SHEET 9
Materials

one small yellow, one small green and one small blue bear, yellow, green and blue coloured pencils

Help the children to read and understand the instructions on the activity sheet. Encourage them to find an orderly manner in which to change the order of the three bears. The children should find six different arrays of bears.
On the another sheet, they can add the fourth colour bear and find out how many different ways they can arrange four bears.

Colour the stools and put bears on them. Find different ways to change the order of the bears, then colour the rest of the stools.

yellow green blue

Small, larger, largest

Aim

To practise sorting, matching, ordering and comparing

Vocabulary

Sort, match, compare, size, large, larger, largest, small, smaller, smallest, same, different

Materials

Three box lids, labels: small, smaller, smallest, large, larger, largest

Activity 1   Small, larger, largest

Put out three lids labelled 'small', 'larger', 'largest'. Read the labels to the children and talk about the difference in the sizes of the bears. Hold a small bear and ask 'Which bears are larger than this bear?' 'How many bears are larger?'

Hold a medium bear and then a large bear and repeat the questions. Then ask, 'Which bears will go in the "small" the "larger" and the "largest" box?'

Let the children sort the bears.

Activity 2   Large, smaller, smallest

Put out three lids labelled 'large', 'smaller', 'smallest'.

Read the labels to the children and talk about the difference in the size of the bears. Repeat Activity 1. Ask, 'Which bears are smaller?' 'Which boxes will they go into?'

Activity 3   Small, smaller, smallest

Put out three lids labelled 'small', 'smaller', 'smallest'. Remind the children of the words. Ask, 'How will you sort the bears this time?' Allow the children plenty of time to talk about this problem. Encourage them to use the correct vocabulary as they sort the bears.

Give the children the labels 'large', 'larger', 'largest'. Read the labels and ask 'How will you sort the bears for these labels?' Allow the children plenty of time to decide and re-sort if necessary. Some children may decide that sorting again is unnecessary, and the boxes can just be re-labelled. This decision must come from the children.

ACTIVITY SHEET 10
Materials

Cut-outs of bears (from p. 93), glue

Help the children to read down the words in the sets. The children compare the bears in the sets until they have sorted the correct bears to the labels. They match the cut-out pictures to the bears, stick them in the sets and colour them.

Extra activities

Ask the children to select among themselves someone to hold the labels: large, larger, largest; and small, smaller and smallest. They can also choose from books, bricks, balls and bottles.

Prepare arrows.

Select a group of five children's bears. Ask the children to place the bears in order with the arrows in between. Talk about the position of each bear, naming the largest and smallest bear. Repeat the activity with labels.

Stick on bears to match the sizes.

large	large	small	small
smaller	larger	larger	smaller
smallest	largest	largest	smallest

Matching bears on grids

Aim

To recognise and copy position on a grid

Vocabulary

Position, grid, row, column, above, below, beside, between, empty, up, down, next to, across

ACTIVITY SHEETS 11 AND 12

Materials

Medium and small bears, coloured pencils, medium and small bear cut-outs

Match the bears to the pictures. Encourage the children to talk about the position of the bears on the grid. Introduce the idea of a row and a column. Look at bears which are above, below, beside and between the empty spaces. Help the children to understand the idea of transferring the bears to the empty grid. Keep the bears in the same position.

ACTIVITY SHEET 13

A game for 2 players

Materials

A set of 12 different bears with another set to match, a bag to hold the second set of bears, one activity sheet for each player

The players put six different bears on the left-hand grid and match each bear exactly on to the second grid. All the bears on the second grid from both players are put into the bag and shaken. Each player in turn takes a bear from the bag. If it matches a bear on the left-hand grid it is placed in exactly the same place on the right-hand grid. If it does not match, the bear is returned to the bag and the turn passes to the other player. The winner is the first player to complete the grid.

Match and colour the medium and small bears on this grid.

Copy the bears on to this grid. Use cut-out pictures of the bears.

Match and colour the medium and small bears on this grid.

Copy the bears on to this grid. Use cut-out pictures of the bears.

Put 6 different bears on this grid.

Match the bears on to this grid.

Sorting with one or two attributes

Aim

To practise sorting with one or two atttributes

Vocabulary

Sort, set, green, not green

Materials

Attribute cards made from cut-out pictures of large, medium and small bears. Draw a cross over the attribute card to indicate the 'not' or negative attribute.

Activity 1

Materials

A set of large bears,
labels: red, blue, green, yellow, not red, not blue, not green, not yellow
A hoop and a sheet of paper

Ask the children to separate the red bears from the rest of the set (one attribute). Look at the remaining bears. They are not red bears. Explain that this set has the negative attribute and is called 'Not red bears'. Put the label for green bears in the hoop. Ask the children to sort the bears on to the paper. Ask 'What do you call the bears outside the hoop? Find a label for them.' Repeat using the other colours.

ACTIVITY SHEET 14

Materials

A set of medium bears, attribute cards

Label the two regions 'yellow' and 'not yellow'. Ask the children to sort the bears. Repeat using the other colours.

ACTIVITY SHEET 15

Materials

The set of 40 small bears, labels: 'red' and 'yellow'

Talk about the diagram and locate three regions: inside the rectangle and inside the two rings. Label the rings red and yellow. Ask the children to sort the small bears into the rings. The remaining bears go outside the rings but inside the rectangle as they all belong to the set of small bears.

ACTIVITY SHEET 16 A VENN DIAGRAM

Materials

A set of large and medium bears, labels: 'blue' and 'large'

Talk about the diagram and locate four regions. Label the two rings 'blue' and 'large'. Ask 'Which bears will go in the large ring? The blue ring? and the middle region?' Remind the children that all the bears must have a place inside the rectangle. Finally, talk about the regions, stating the bears they have and do not have.

ACTIVITY SHEET 17 A CARROLL DIAGRAM

Materials

five blue and five green small bears,
five blue and five green medium bears,
labels: blue, not blue, small, not small

Place the small labels across the top and the colour labels down the side of the diagram. Ask the children to describe the bears which will go into each of the four regions. Repeat using other bears and colours.

ACTIVITY SHEET 18 A SORTING TREE

Materials

two red, two blue, two green and two yellow small bears,
two red, two blue, two green and two yellow medium bears;
labels: yellow, not yellow, medium, not medium

Talk about the diagram with the children. Explain that the bears climb the tree to reach the tree houses. The instructions tell them which branch they climb. Describe the bears in each house and the reasons for their choice.

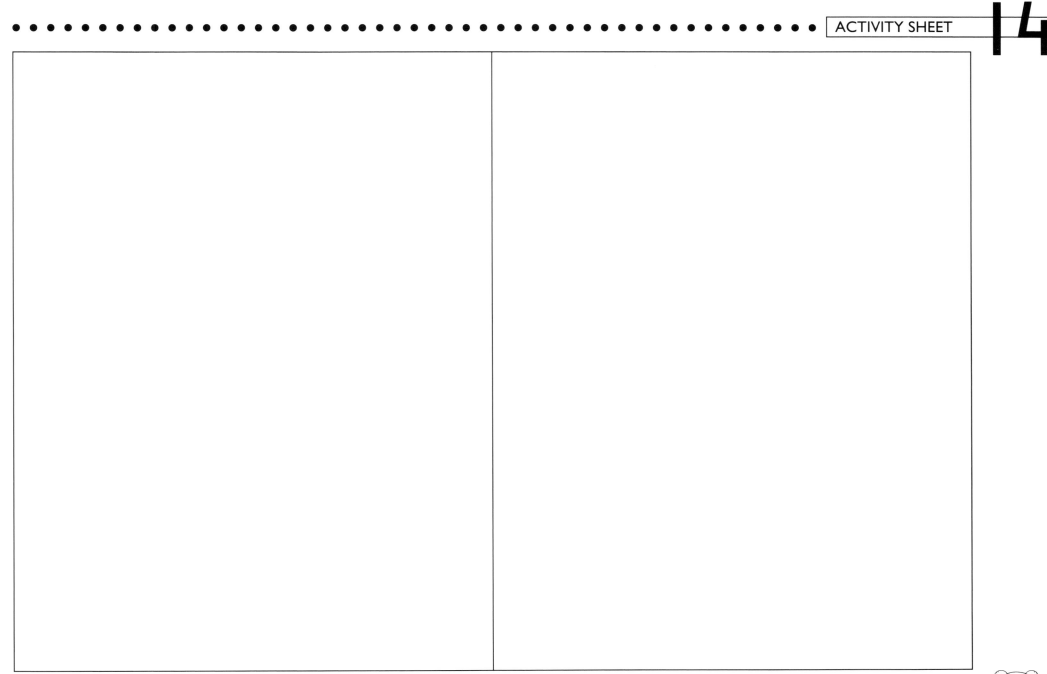

© LDA Compare Bears Maths Book 1

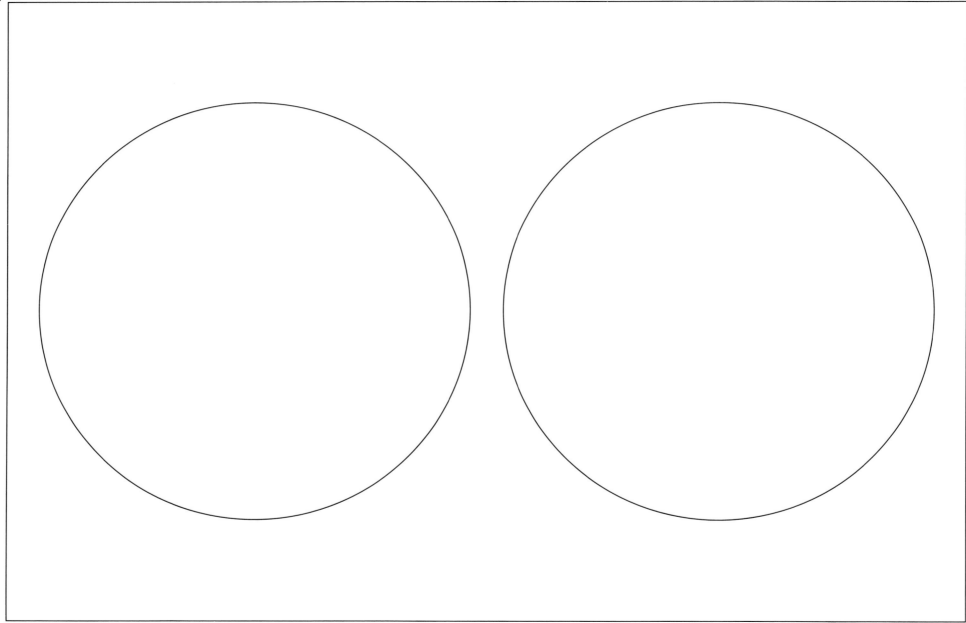

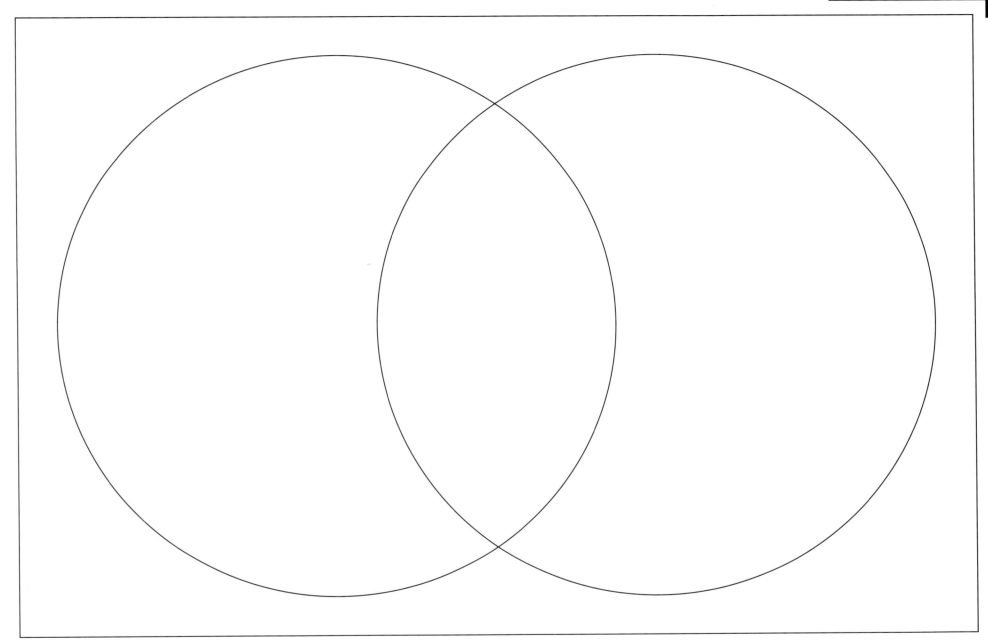

© LDA Compare Bears Maths Book 1

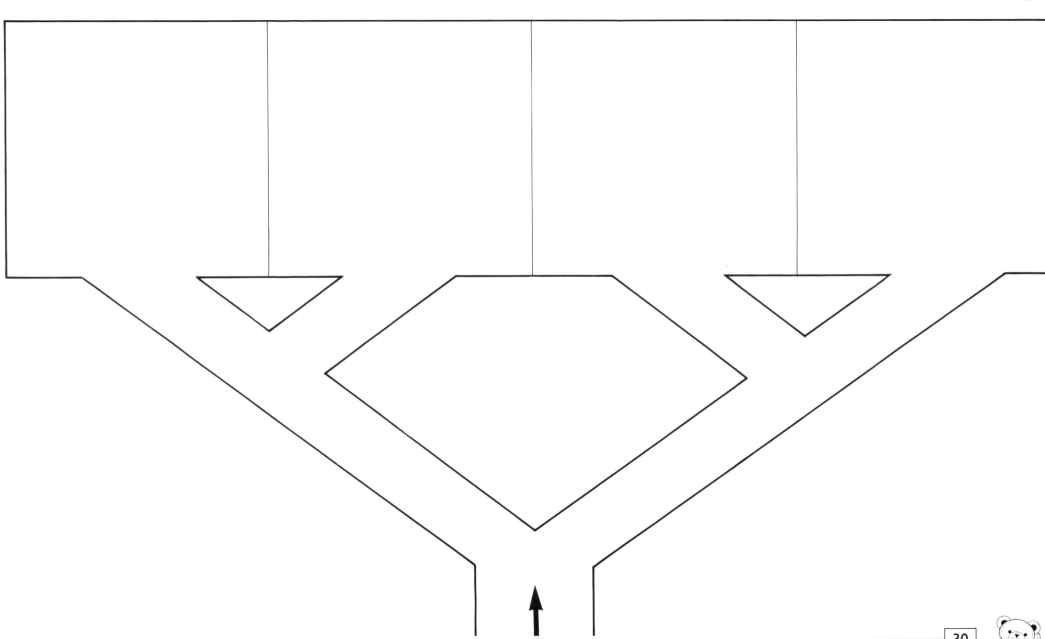

Continue the pattern

Aim

To practise continuing patterns in size and colour

Vocabulary

Continue, repeat, pattern, the same, different, before, after, next

Activity 1   Two sizes

Put out three large blue and three small blue bears. Place them in a row: one large, one small, one large, one small ...
Talk about the size and colour of the bears in the row. Ask 'Is there a pattern in the size or colour of the bears? Is the size of the bears repeated? Are the colours repeated? How will you continue the row?'
Ask the children to copy the row and continue the pattern.

Activity 2   Two colours

Put out three blue and three red medium bears. Place them in a row one red, one blue, one red, one blue .... Talk about the colours and the sizes of the bears. Ask 'Which can you repeat: the colour or the size?'
Ask the children to copy the row and continue the pattern.

Activity 3   All sorts

Continue to make up patterns for the children to copy and continue.
For example:

1 size	3 colours	3 sizes	1 colour
1 size	4 colours	3 sizes	2 colours
2 sizes	2 colours	3 sizes	3 colours
2 sizes	3 colours	3 sizes	4 colours
2 sizes	4 colours		

Ask the children to make up their own repeating patterns for their friends to copy. Encourage them to describe the patterns they make and how the sequence will continue.

ACTIVITY SHEET 19

Materials

Cut-out pictures of the bears (from p. 93), glue, coloured pencils

The children match the bears on to the pictures and continue the pattern. They select the pictures to match the bears, stick them in place and colour them. The first two lines are patterns in size and the children should be encouraged to mix the colours. The last line is more complicated, with two sizes and three colours.

Continue the line of bears. Keep them in the same order. Colour the bears.

red   blue   red   blue   red

Bears on the balance

Aim

To estimate which bears are heavier/ lighter and check using a balance

Vocabulary

Heavy, heavier, light, lighter, balance, weighs the same, weight, same, different, balance, left, right, order, arrow

Materials

A 'see-saw' style balance, labels:

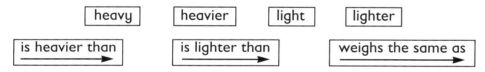

Activity 1   Heavy and light

Encourage the children to talk about the things around them which are heavy and the things which are light. Ask the children to choose two bears and say which one they think is heavy and which one they think is light. Let them test their estimates on the balance, and then place the bears in the right set.

heavy   light

Ask the children to look at the bears in the heavy set (the large and medium) and the bears in the light set (the medium and small). Ask 'Why are the medium bears in both sets?'

Activity 2   Heavier and lighter

Read the card 'is heavier than'. Ask the children to choose two bears and place the card and the bears in the right order. Use the balance to check their estimate. Encourage the children to name the bears and read the card. For example, 'The large bear is heavier than the medium bear.' Repeat the activity several times.
Introduce the arrow 'is lighter than' and ask the children to choose two bears and place them in order with the arrow. Check their estimate with the balance.
Encourage each child to read the cards and name the bears several times.

Activity 3   The same weight

Read the card to the children and ask them to choose two bears which they think have the same weight. Place them on the table with the arrow. Check with the balance. Encourage the children to read the card and name the bears. This activity can be extended to weighing several bears at a time, for example, 'two small bears weigh the same as two small bears.'

[ACTIVITY SHEET 20]
Materials

Balance, coloured pencils, cut-out pictures of the bears (p. 93), glue

Ask the children to say which end of the see-saw will have a heavy bear and which a light bear. Let the children check their decision with the balance before they stick one bear only at each end of the balance.

Stick one bear on each end of the see-saw

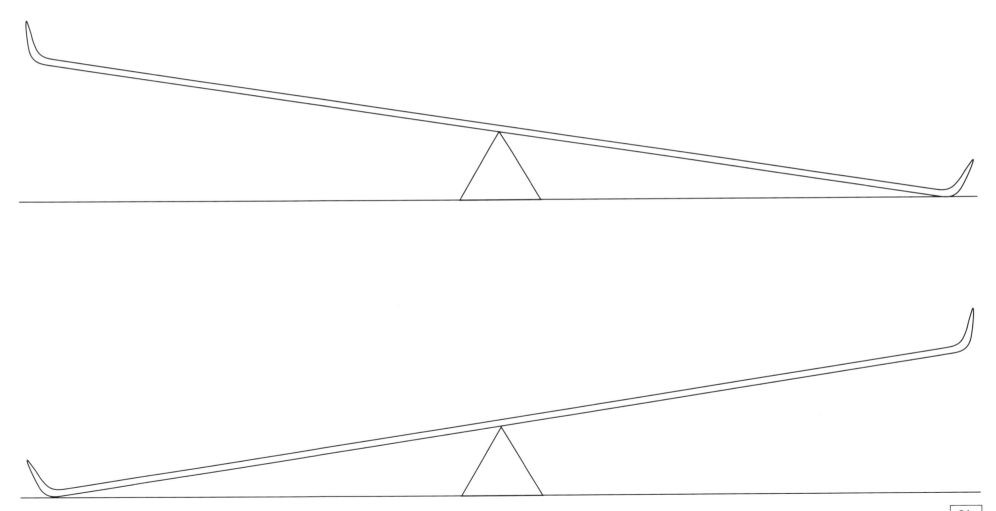

Light, heavier, heaviest

Aim

To compare the weight of individual bears

Vocabulary

Light, lighter, lightest, heavy, heavier, heaviest, weight, weigh, weighs the same, compare, order

Materials

Balance, cards: light, lighter, lightest, heavy, heavier, heaviest

Activity 1   Heaviest, lightest

Put out a set of bears and 3 rings labelled 'heavy', 'lighter', 'lightest'. Ask the children to read the cards and sort the bears into the rings. Name the bears in the rings: 'The large bears are heavy. The medium bears are lighter. The small bears are lightest.'
Introduce the cards 'light', 'heavier', 'heaviest', read them and ask the children to sort the bears. Some children may suggest just changing the labels but some children will need to weigh and re-sort the bears again.

Activity 2   Order the bears

Put out a set of bears, balance and arrows: 'is heavier than'; 'is lighter than'; 'weighs the same as'. Ask the children to make lines of bears using the arrows.

Activity 3   Light, lighter, lightest, heavy, heavier, heaviest

Put out the set of bears. Read and talk about the labels light, lighter, lightest. Ask the children to find three bears to fit the labels.
Allow plenty of time for them to talk about calling a large bear 'light'. Repeat the activity with the 'heavy', 'heavier', 'heaviest' cards.

ACTIVITY SHEET 21

Materials

Cut-out pictures, glue, coloured pencils

Help the children to read the words in the sets. The children compare bears in the sets until they have the correct bears to match the labels. They match cut-out pictures to the bears, stick them in the sets and colour them.

Extra activities

The children can use their own teddy bears to estimate which is the 'heavy' and 'heavier' and the 'light' and 'lighter' and then use the balance to check their estimates. In the same way, they can label their bears 'light', 'lighter' and 'lightest' or 'heavy', 'heavier, heaviest'. They can put their bears in order using the arrows 'is heavier than', 'is lighter than', 'weighs the same as'.
The children can compare, estimate and order items in the classroom and apparatus in P.E.

Stick on the bears to match the weights.

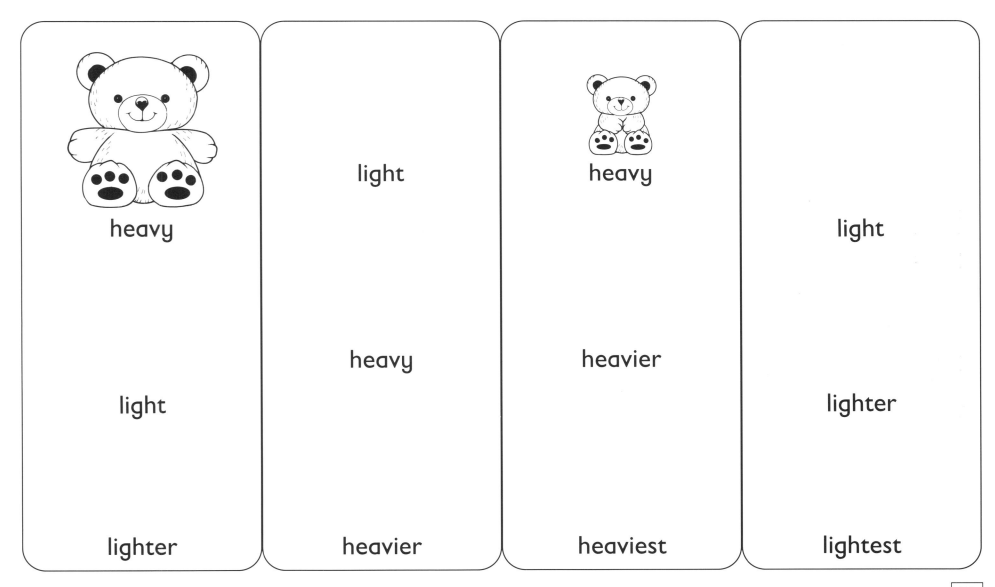

heavy

light

lighter

light

heavy

heavier

heavy

heavier

heaviest

light

lighter

lightest

© LDA Compare Bears Maths Book 1

Weighs more than, weighs less than

Aim

To compare the weight of one bear with a combined weight of bears

Vocabulary

How many, too many, too few, too much, too little, more, less, the same as, enough, weighs more, weighs less

Materials

Balance

Activity 1   Weighs the same

Put out two large, four medium and six small bears. Hold up one large bear and ask the children to guess how many small bears will balance the large bear. Ask a child to balance the large with the small bears. Ask 'Who guessed three bears? More bears? Fewer bears?' Repeat the activity. Use all the bears and balance them against each other.

ACTIVITY SHEET 22
Materials

Three large, four medium, six small bears; cut-out pictures, glue, balance

Read the words on the arrows with the children. Ask them to place the bears on the sheet and read aloud the statement, '1 large bear weighs the same as 3 small bears' before selecting the correct pictures and sticking them on the line.

Activity 2   Weighs more than

Put out several large, medium and small bears, and a balance. Ask the children to complete the sentences, 'A large bear weighs more than ...' and 'A medium bear weighs more than ...' Use the balance to check.

ACTIVITY SHEET 23
Materials

Cut-out pictures, glue, a balance

Read the words on the arrow with the children. Ask them to place the bears on the sheet and read aloud the statement about the bears, 'one large bear weighs more than one medium bear'.

Activity 3   Weighs less than

Put out several large, medium and small bears and a balance. Ask the children to complete the sentences, 'one small bear weighs less than ....' and 'one medium bear weighs less than ...' Use the balance to check.

ACTIVITY SHEET 24
Materials

Cut-out pictures, glue, a balance

Read the words on the arrow with the children. Place the bears on the sheet and read aloud the sentence, 'one small bear weighs less than one medium bear'.

Extra activities

The children can use their own teddy bears. Ask 'Can you find:
two bears which weigh the same as one bear?
two bears which weigh more than one bear?
two bears which weigh less than one bear?'

Weigh the bears.
Match the pictures and stick them on the line.

weighs the same as

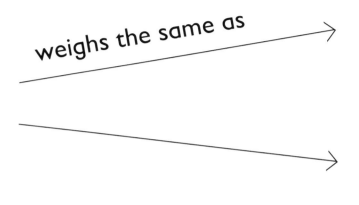

_____

_____

I large bear

balances

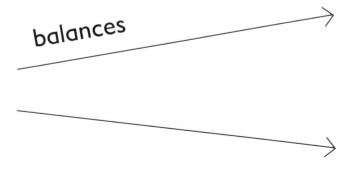

_____

_____

I medium bear

• •

Weigh the bears.
Match the pictures and stick them on the line.

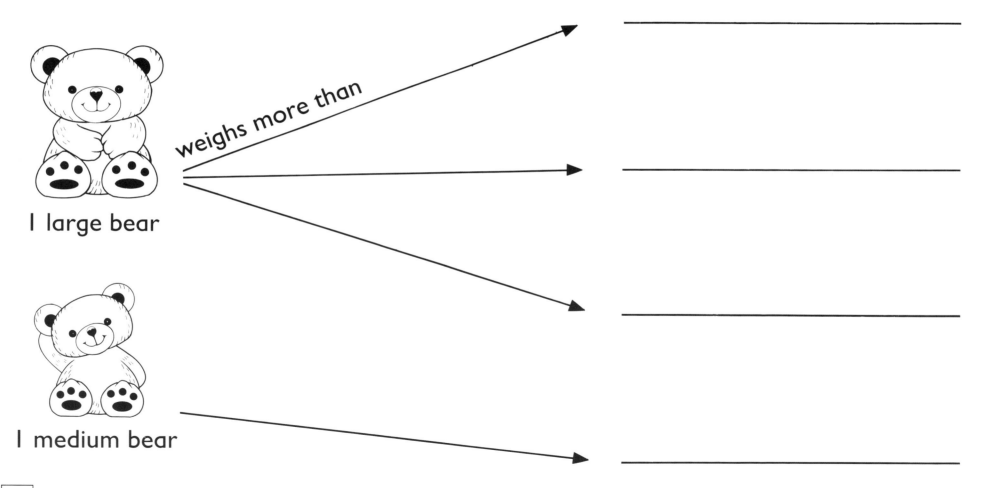

I large bear

weighs more than

I medium bear

Weigh the bears.
Match the pictures and stick them on the line.

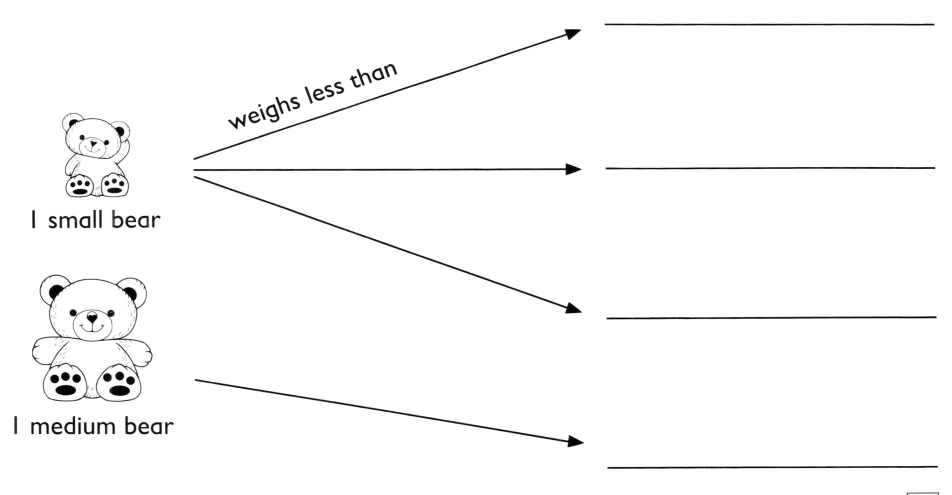

I small bear

weighs less than

I medium bear

Weigh several bears

Aim

To weigh several bears together

Vocabulary

More, fewer, too many, too few, how many, more, less, the same, enough, weighs more, weighs less

Materials

Balance

Activity 1   The large bears

Hold the large bear and ask the children to say which other bears will balance with it. Check using the balance. Ask 'How many medium bears will balance two large bears?' Encourage the children to weigh several bears at a time.

Activity 2   Weighs more

Reintroduce the arrow 'weighs more than' and ask the children to find bears to fit the arrow using two and three bears at a time. For example, 'Three small bears weigh more than one medium bear.' Encourage them to estimate before using the balance.

After the children have experienced weighing several bears at a time, introduce the idea of 'the larger number'. For example, 'Five large bears weigh more than two large bears.' Line up and compare the bears. Look at the number line to see that 5 is more than 2.

Activity 3   Weighs less

Re-introduce the arrow 'weighs less than'. Repeat Activity 2. Line up and compare the bears: 'Two large bears weigh less than four large bears. 2 is less than 4. Look at the number line.'

ACTIVITY SHEET 25

Materials

Balance

Some children may need help with reading the words on the sheet.

Extra activities

The children can use arbitrary units such as bricks, bolts or bean bags to weigh their own teddy bears. By using the same units to weigh two bears, they can discover which bear weighs more.
Make a graph of the weight of some of the children's bears.
Let them use gummed paper squares to represent the bricks.

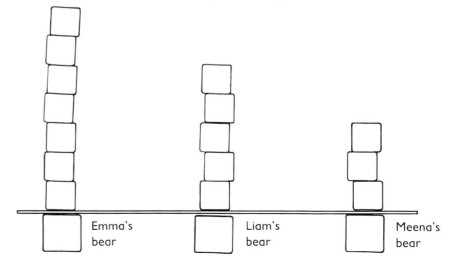

Weigh the bears.

weighs the same as →

1 large bear   ————————————→ ———— small bears

2 large bears   ————————————→ ———— small bears

2 large bears   ————————————→ ———— medium bears

3 large bears   ————————————→ ———— small bears

4 large bears   ————————————→ ———— medium bears

1 medium bear   ————————————→ ———— small bears

2 medium bears   ————————————→ ———— small bears

3 medium bears   ————————————→ ———— large bears

Add, group and subtract the bears

Aims

To add together two sets of bears, to make two groups and to subtract bears

Vocabulary

Add, equals, how many, altogether, answer box, sum, total

Materials

Number cards

Activity 1   How many?

Put out six bears. Ask the children to count them and match each bear to a number card. Take two bears and say 'Here are two bears. Add one more bear. How many bears altogether?' Show the children how the sum is written. Use + which says 'plus' and = which says 'equals'. Point to the cards 2 + 1 = 3 and read 'Two plus one equals three.' Repeat this activity using all the combinations of 6.

ACTIVITY SHEET 26
Materials

Six bears

Remind the children that + says 'plus' and = says 'equals'. Ask them to read the first sum, 'one plus one equals'. Tell them to take one bear and one bear and place them on the number line. Write the total in the answer box.

Activity 2   Make two groups

Ask the children to take five bears each. 'Put the bears into two groups. Make your groups different from your friend's groups.' Ask each child to say the number of bears in each group and how many there are altogether. 'Two plus three equals five'. Repeat the activity, covering all the groups from 0 and 5 to 4 and 1.

ACTIVITY SHEET 27
Materials

Six bears

The children place six bears in the spaces above the numbers. They make two groups from the six bears, as they did in Activity 2 and write the numbers in the boxes, 1 + 5 = 6. Encourage the children to find an order in the way they make the groups: 1 and 5, 2 and 4 and so on. Ask the children to read the number sentences when they have finished.

Activity 3   Subtract the bears

Ask the children to take 5 bears each. Say 'Take some of your bears for a walk and count how many you have left.' Encourage the children to tell a story, for example: 'I had five bears, I took four for a walk and left one behind.' Put out cards 5 – 4 = 1. Explain that – means take away or minus. Read 'Five minus four equals one.' Repeat the activity including zero: 'It was raining so no bears went for a walk. Five minus zero equals five.'

WORKSHEET 28
Materials

Six bears

Remind the children that – means take away or minus. They place six bears in the spaces above the numbers and complete the sums by taking away a different number of bears each time.

Add the bears.

1	2	3	4	5	6

1 + 1 = ☐   1 + 4 = ☐

1 + 2 = ☐   1 + 5 = ☐

1 + 3 = ☐   2 + 1 = ☐

Make 2 groups of the bears.

1	2	3	4	5	6

☐ + ☐ = 6   ☐ + ☐ = 6

☐ + ☐ = 6   ☐ + ☐ = 6

☐ + ☐ = 6   ☐ + ☐ = 6

Take away some bears.

1	2	3	4	5	6

6 – ☐ = ☐   6 – ☐ = ☐

6 – ☐ = ☐   6 – ☐ = ☐

6 – ☐ = ☐   6 – ☐ = ☐

Numbers up to 10

Aim

To practise counting and ordering numbers to 7, 8, 9 and 10

Vocabulary

Seven, eight, nine, ten, count on, count back, how many, altogether, backwards

Materials

Cards 0 to 7, +, –, =

Activity 1   Seven Compare Bears

Put out seven small bears. Point to them and count with the children. Explain '7 is 1 more than 6.' Ask the children to put cards 0 to 7 in order and match the bears to them. Say 'Now give each small bear a medium bear and a large bear. How many medium bears? How many large bears? Count again. Count backwards.' Ask the children to take seven bears each and line them up. Count again. Ask 'Which number comes after 6, after 5, after 4, ...? Which number comes before 7, before 6, before 5 ...?'

Activity 2   Seven in two groups

Ask the children to take seven bears each. 'Put them into two groups. How many bears in each group? How many bears altogether? Say what you have done and the sum you have made.' '4 plus 3 equals 7.'
Find the cards 4 + 3 = 7 and put them beside the bears. How many different groups can you make?

Activity 3   Take away some bears

Ask the children to take seven bears each. Say 'Take some of the bears shopping. Count the bears you have left. Say what you have done and the sum you have made: I have seven bears. I took four shopping. I left three behind. 7 minus 4 equals 3.'
Repeat the activity. Change the number of bears taken away. Tell the story, say the sum. How many different sums are there for 7? Find a pattern, put them in order.

ACTIVITY SHEETS 29 TO 36   ADD AND TAKE AWAY

These activity sheets have the same structure as the previous three sheets, so they will be familiar to the children. The activities for the numbers 6 and 7 must be repeated when each new number is introduced. For some children the numbers 7, 8, 9 and 10 take a long time to understand and remember.
Give the children plenty of time to practise each number before going on to the next. For children who find these numbers particularly difficult, Activities on p. 11 'Counting to 5' and p. 13 'Counting to 6' can be repeated.
Encourage the children to find a pattern and an order in the addition and subtraction sums. Ask them to 'read' the sums aloud when they have completed the activity sheets.

ACTIVITY SHEET 37

Aim
To find the right order of numbers 1 to 10

Vocabulary
Join, missing numbers

Materials
Coloured pencils

Encourage the children to find the numbers and follow the order with a finger before they use a pencil to join up the dots and squares.

Add the bears.

1	2	3	4	5	6	7

$1 + \square = 7$ $5 + \square = 7$

$2 + \square = 7$ $6 + \square = 7$

$3 + \square = 7$ $7 + \square = 7$

$4 + \square = 7$ $\square + 1 = 7$

$0 + \square = 7$ $\square + 2 = 7$

Take away some bears.

1	2	3	4	5	6	7

7 − ☐ = ☐   7 − ☐ = ☐

7 − ☐ = ☐   7 − ☐ = ☐

7 − ☐ = ☐   7 − ☐ = ☐

7 − ☐ = ☐   ☐ − 3 = 4

7 − ☐ = ☐   ☐ − 2 = 5

Make 2 groups of the bears.

1	2	3	4	5	6	7	8

☐ + ☐ = 8   ☐ + ☐ = 8

☐ + ☐ = 8   ☐ + ☐ = 8

☐ + ☐ = 8   ☐ + ☐ = 8

☐ + ☐ = 8   ☐ + 7 = 8

☐ + ☐ = 8   ☐ + 6 = 8

Take away some bears.

1	2	3	4	5	6	7	8

8 − ☐ = ☐   8 − ☐ = ☐

8 − ☐ = ☐   8 − ☐ = ☐

8 − ☐ = ☐   8 − ☐ = ☐

8 − ☐ = ☐   8 − ☐ = ☐

8 − ☐ = ☐   ☐ − 1 = 7

Make 2 groups of the bears.

1	2	3	4	5	6	7	8	9

$\square$ + $\square$ = 9 $\square$ + $\square$ = 9

$\square$ + $\square$ = 9 $\square$ + $\square$ = 9

$\square$ + $\square$ = 9 $\square$ + $\square$ = 9

$\square$ + $\square$ = 9 $\square$ + $\square$ = 9

$\square$ + $\square$ = 9 $\square$ + $\square$ = 9

© LDA Compare Bears Maths Book 1

Take away some bears.

1	2	3	4	5	6	7	8	9

9 – ☐ = ☐   9 – ☐ = ☐

9 – ☐ = ☐   9 – ☐ = ☐

9 – ☐ = ☐   9 – ☐ = ☐

9 – ☐ = ☐   9 – ☐ = ☐

9 – ☐ = ☐   9 – ☐ = ☐

Make different groups of 10 baby bears.

1	2	3	4	5	6	7	8	9	10

☐ + ☐ = 10   ☐ + ☐ = 10

☐ + ☐ = 10   ☐ + ☐ = 10

☐ + ☐ = 10   ☐ + ☐ = 10

☐ + ☐ = 10   ☐ + ☐ = 10

☐ + ☐ = 10   ☐ + ☐ = 10

Take away some small bears.

1	2	3	4	5	6	7	8	9	10

10 − ☐ = ☐   10 − ☐ = ☐

10 − ☐ = ☐   10 − ☐ = ☐

10 − ☐ = ☐   10 − ☐ = ☐

10 − ☐ = ☐   10 − ☐ = ☐

10 − ☐ = ☐   10 − ☐ = ☐

Join ● 1 to 10.

Join □ 1 to 10.

Fill in the missing numbers.

Colour your picture.

© LDA Compare Bears Maths Book 1

Sorting on to the grid and changing the colour

Aim

To practise sorting the bears on to a grid using two attributes, colour and size; to practise changing one attribute at a time

Vocabulary

Sort, colour, size, row, column, change

Materials

One bear of each colour and size, cut-outs of all three sizes (p. 93), glue, coloured pencils

ACTIVITY SHEET 38

Talk about the grid with the children. Read the colour headings and the rows, small, medium and large. Show the children how to draw a finger along the small bear row to each colour column and how to decide which bear belongs in each space. Replace the bears with cut-outs; glue and colour them on the grid.

ACTIVITY SHEET 39

Place a bear of any size or colour in the centre circle. The double lines radiating from it say 'change the colour' (not the size). Place three bears of the same size in the adjacent circles. A single line says 'change the size' (not the colour). Continue to place bears in the circles according to the instruction given by the line until all the circles are occupied. When the children understand the instructions to change the size or the colour, suggest that they try placing the first bear in different circles.

Sort the bears on to the grid.

colour / size	red	blue	green	yellow
small				
medium				
large				

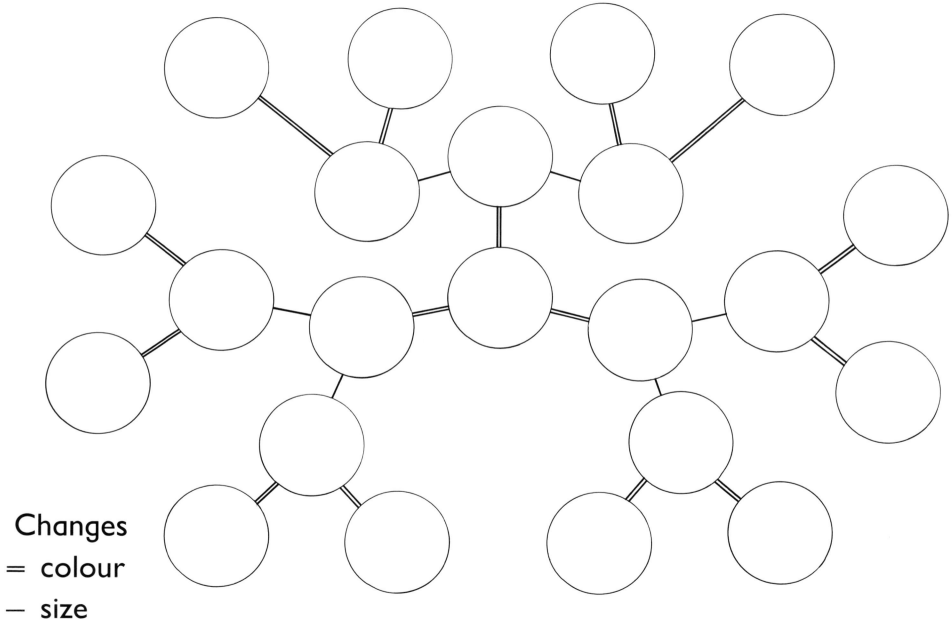

Changes

= colour

− size

Find 1 bear of each colour and size. Place them evenly and in order round the table.

Draw a stool for each bear.

Draw on the table a plate, and a mug, for each bear.

Colour them to match the bears.

© LDA Compare Bears Maths Book 1

Square and triangular picnic cloths

Aim

To practise choosing the appropriate attribute by which to sort the bears

Vocabulary

Square, triangle, shape, sides, group

Materials

12 bears, one of each colour and size

ACTIVITY SHEETS 40 AND 41

The children find one bear of each colour and size and sort them into colour groups. Ask 'How many red bears, blue bears, green bears and yellow bears? How many bears altogether? How many different colour groups?' Re-sort the bears into size groups. How many large bears? Medium bears? Small bears? How many bears altogether? How many different groups?' At the first picnic there is a square cloth. The children arrange the bears round the square, with one group on each side. Put the bears in the same order on each side.

At the next picnic there is a triangular cloth. Arrange the bears on three sides. Keep them in order round the cloth.

Children draw and colour stools to match the bears. They then draw and colour plates and mugs to match. If the children are able, they can be asked to draw the mugs on the right-hand side of the plate and the spoons on the left-hand side.

Find 1 bear of each colour and size. Place them evenly and in order round the table.

Draw their stools. Draw on the table a dish and a spoon for each bear.

Colour them to match the bear.

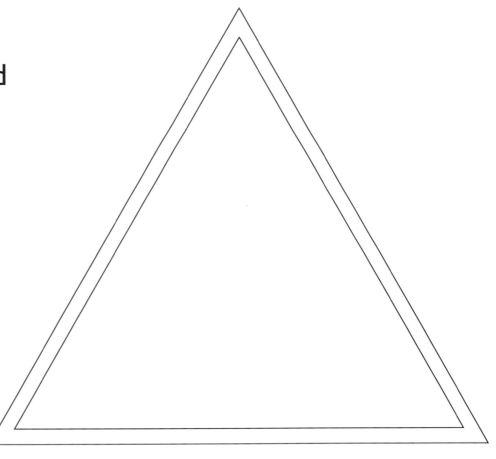

© LDA Compare Bears Maths Book 1

A handful of bears

Aim

To use the bears to measure area

Vocabulary

Cover, fit inside, draw round, how many, overlap, too many, too few, not enough, space, same amount, same number, surface, position

Materials

A4 cards and envelopes

Activity 1 How many bears?

Fold and cut a sheet of coloured A4 paper into six pieces. Establish with the children that the pieces are all the same size. Give the children a piece of paper each and ask them to cover the paper with bears. Let the children mix the size, colour and positions (lying or sitting) of the bears. 'Count the bears on your paper.' Ask each child to say the number of large, medium and small bears they used and how they were positioned on the paper. Compare the different totals and methods of covering. Make a list.

Emma used ☐ bears to cover

Liam used ☐ ⟶

Meena used ☐ ⟶

Activity 2 One size only

Ask the children to choose only one size of bear. Ask them to estimate first how many bears will cover the paper. The bears can sit or lie. Make a list. Record the estimate and then how many bears it actually took to cover the paper. Talk about the estimates and totals. Encourage the children to discuss the reasons for the difference in the number of large bears and small bears and whether they are lying or sitting.

Activity 3 A handful of bears

Ask the children to count the number of bears they can pick up in one hand, and to name the colour and size. Ask the children to stand the bears on one of their own hands held out flat. Ask 'Have you enough bears to cover your hand? Not enough? Too many? How many more do you need?' Give the children other areas such as small books to cover.

ACTIVITY SHEET 42   DRAW YOUR HAND

Show the children how to draw round their hands. Assist them if necessary. The children cover the area of the hand using the three different sizes of bears separately. Can they explain why the three totals are different? Compare the different totals of all the children. Make graphs. Whose hand is largest/smallest? Is the result the same with medium and small bears?

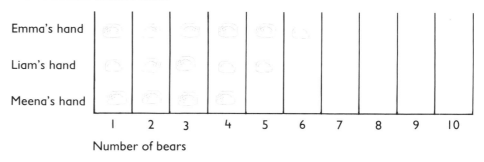

Emma's hand

Liam's hand

Meena's hand

1 2 3 4 5 6 7 8 9 10

Number of bears

Draw round your hand.

☐ large bears will sit on my hand

☐ medium bears will sit on my hand

☐ small bears will sit on my hand

Short, taller, tallest

Aim

To compare the height of the bears

Vocabulary

Tall, taller, short, shorter, height, tallest, shortest, the same, back to back

Materials

Labels: tall   taller   tallest
           short   shorter   stortest

Activity I   Taller and shorter

Place a large and small bear back to back. Ask which bear is taller. The small bear is 'tall' but the large bear is 'taller'. Ask a child to find the labels, read them aloud and place them beside the bears. Ask another child to find different bears and place the labels beside them. Repeat the activity using the 'short' and 'shorter' labels. Ask 'Which bears are taller than the small bear, medium bear and large bear?' Ask 'Which bears are shorter than the large bear, medium bear and small bear?'

ACTIVITY SHEET 43

Materials

Coloured pencils

The children match bears to the stools, colour the stool of the taller/shorter bear and then complete the sentences.

Activity 2   Tallest, shortest, the same

Line up a large, medium and small bear.
Ask 'Which bear is taller than the small bear? Which bear is taller than the medium bear? Is there a bear taller than the large bear? Which bear is the tallest?' Ask a child to find labels for the bears and read 'tall', 'taller', 'tallest'.
Repeat the activity using the 'short', 'shorter' and 'shortest' labels.
Hold up a large bear and ask the children to show you a bear with the same height. Repeat with the medium and small bears.

ACTIVITY SHEETS 44, 45 AND 46

Materials

Coloured pencils, cut-outs for Activity Sheets 45 and 46

The children match the bears to the stools, colour the stool of the tallest/shortest bear and complete the sentences. Encourage the children to read the worksheets when they have completed them.

ACTIVITY SHEET 47

There are 16 different arrays for these bears. Children who find more than are shown can turn over and work on the back of the sheet.

Sit the bears back to back on the stools. Colour the stool for the taller bear.

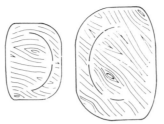

a _____ bear is taller than a small bear.

a _____ bear is taller than a medium bear.

a _____ bear is taller than a small bear.

Sit the bears back to back on the stools. Colour the stool for the shorter bear.

a _____ bear is shorter than a medium bear

and a _____ bear is shorter than a large bear.

Colour the stool of the tallest bear.

a _____ bear is the tallest

Colour the stool of the shortest bear.

a _____ bear is the shortest

Colour the stools of the bears which are the same height.

The _____ bears are the same height

The _____ bears are the same height

The _____ bears are the same height

Stick a large bear, medium bear and small bear in each set.

tall   shorter   shortest

short   taller   tallest

Stick a large bear, medium bear and small bear in each set.

short   shorter   shortest

tall   taller   tallest

Take 4 red and 4 blue small bears. Line them up in 4s. Make each line different. Colour the boxes.

red	red	red	red

blue	blue	blue	blue

red	red	red	blue

Odd and even numbers

Aim

To introduce odd and even numbers

Vocabulary

Odd, even, pair, partner, twos

Materials

Labels: odd and even

Activity 1   Odd and even

Ask the children to take ten bears and line them up so that each bear has a partner. Talk about the pairs. How many in one pair? How many in two pairs? These are even numbers. Each bear has a partner. Ask a child to take one bear alone, without a partner. 1 is an odd number. Place the 'odd' label beside the bear. Take two bears. They make a pair. 2 is an even number. Place the 'even' label beside the bears.
Ask 'Is the next number, 3, odd or even?' Continue to take the bears separately as the children decide if the number is odd or even.

ACTIVITY SHEET 48

Materials

Yellow and green bears, coloured pencils

Working with two colours should help the children to see the difference between odd and even numbers.

ACTIVITY SHEET 49

Materials

Red and green bears, coloured pencils

Some children may need help with reading this activity sheet.

ACTIVITY SHEET 50   ODDS AND EVENS GAME

Materials

one red and one blue bear, one die

Rules

Players roll the die in turn.
Odd numbers on the die move right.
Even numbers on the die move left.
Bears cannot move backwards. They cannot share a stool. A player may have to miss a turn if the bear cannot be moved.
The winner is the first bear home.

You need 6 green and 4 yellow bears.
Match the bears, colour the stools, count in 2s.

green	yellow	green	yellow	green
green	yellow	green	yellow	green

| 2 | ☐ | ☐ | ☐ | ☐ |

Put the bears on the steps.
Count them.
Write odd or even under the number.

			green
		yellow	green
	green	yellow	green
yellow	green	yellow	green

| 1 | ☐ | ☐ | ☐ |
| odd | | | |

Match the bears. Are the numbers odd or even?

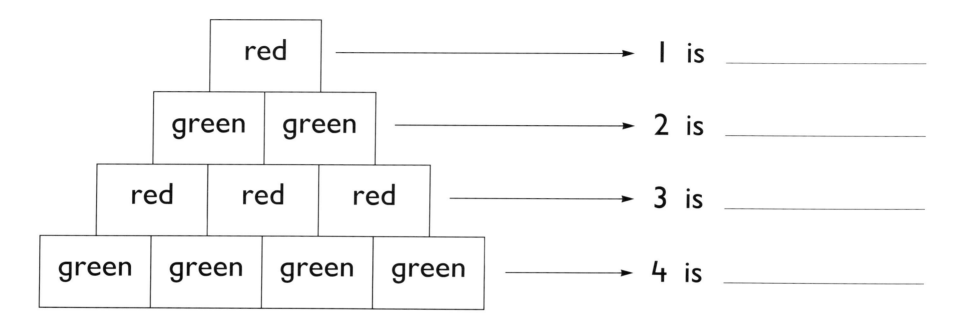

red	→	1 is _____
green green	→	2 is _____
red red red	→	3 is _____
green green green green	→	4 is _____

Line up the bears in pairs.

How many pairs of bears? ☐

How many bears altogether? ☐

Write the odd numbers. _____

Write the even numbers. _____

73

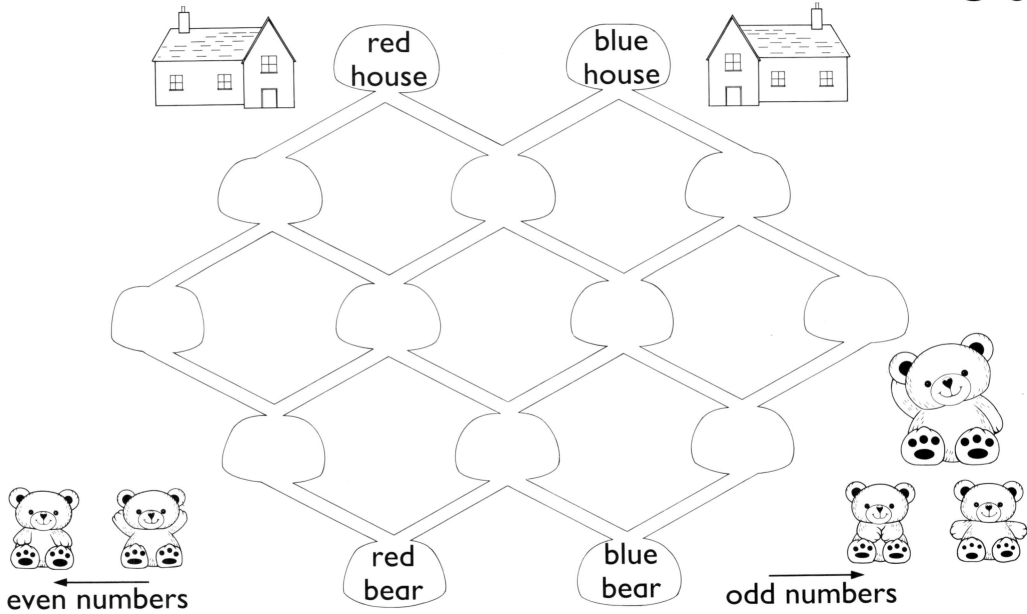

red house

blue house

red bear

blue bear

even numbers

odd numbers

Counting in 2s

Aim

To count in 2s

Vocabulary

Pairs, odd, even, number

Activity 1   How many pairs?

Ask the children to put out a pair of bears. Ask 'How many in a pair?'
Remind the children of odd and even numbers. Put out another pair.
Ask 'How many pairs now? How many altogether?' Put out up to five
pairs. Count the pairs. Count the bears.

ACTIVITY SHEET 51

The children match the bears to the stools by size and colour. Fill in the
numbers in the squares and make up the pairs of bears.

Put the bears on their stools. Match the size and colour.
Put the bears in pairs in the squares. Count in 2s.

1	2
3	—
—	—
—	—
—	—

red

yellow

red

blue

blue

green

yellow

green

red

red

How many pairs of bears? ☐

How many bears altogether? ☐

© LDA Compare Bears Maths Book 1

The addition square

Aim

To practise addition and introduce the idea of rows and columns

Vocabulary

Addition, square, row, column, answer

ACTIVITY SHEET 52

Explain to the children how the line of numbers on the top row are added to the side numbers. Show them how to place a finger on the side number and move it along the row adding the number at the top of each column and writing the answer in the square. Encourage them to put bears at the top of each column and at the side of each row so that they can 'see' how many to count.

ACTIVITY SHEET 53 ADDITION TO 10

Materials

10 bears

The children read the sum 'Three plus two plus four plus one equals', put bears into the numbered squares, and then read off the answer.

ACTIVITY SHEET 54 ROUND AND ROUND THE GARDEN

A game for two players

Materials

one large, one medium, one small bear in two different colours; one die

Rules

The players choose a colour and a home and place the bears in the chairs. They throw the die in turn and move the bears round the garden path. Players do not have to wait for one bear to complete the journey before another bear is started round the path. Scores cannot be divided between two bears and the correct score must be thrown for the final return home.

ACTIVITY SHEET 55 FOUR IN A LINE

A game for two players

Rules

Each player has four bears in one colour. The object of the game is to place the 4 bears in a line – horizontally, vertically or diagonally on the board – and, at the same time prevent the opponent from making a line of four bears. Players take it in turns to place a bear.

ACTIVITY SHEET 56 CIRCLES

A game for two players

Materials

Eight red bears and eight green bears, two dice

Players complete one side of the board

Rules

The players throw the dice in turn, calculate the sum of the scores and place a bear on the corresponding circle. If the score is not shown on the player's circles then the turn is missed. The winner is the first player to cover all the circles.

Use the bears to help fill in the addition square.

Choose a number from the top row and add the number from the side.

Write the answer in the square.

+	1	2	3	4	5
1					
2				6	
3					
4			7		
5					

Place the bears in the squares and count them.

1	2	3	4	5	6	7	8	9	10

3 + 2 + 4 + 1 = ☐

4 + 0 + 3 + 2 = ☐

2 + 2 + 3 + 0 = ☐

3 + 1 + 0 + 4 = ☐

5 + 2 + 1 + 2 = ☐

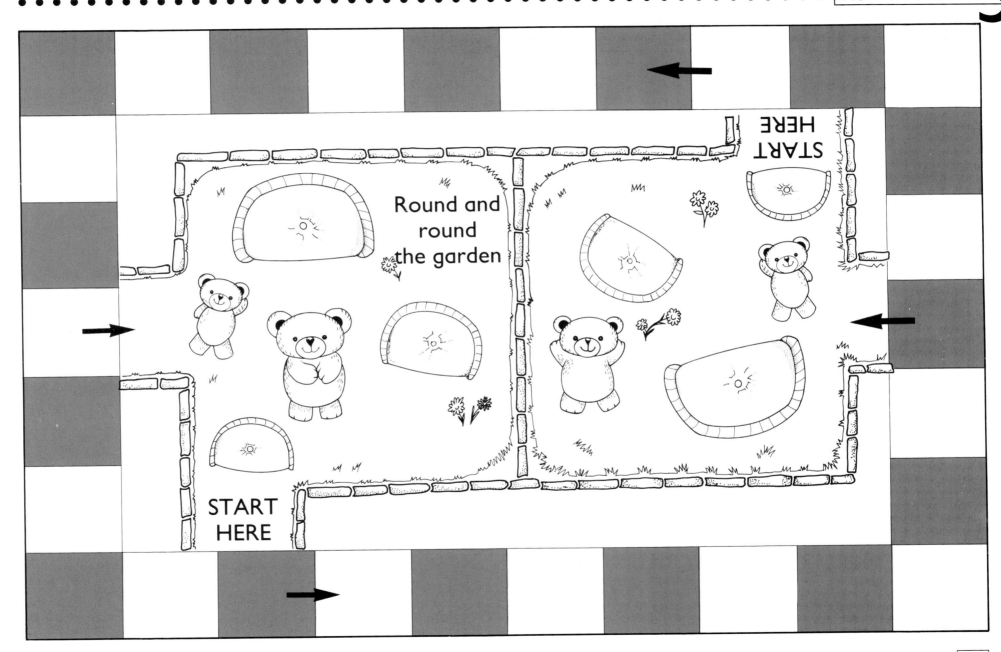

Round and
round
the garden

START
HERE

STΑRT
HΕRΕ

Four in a line

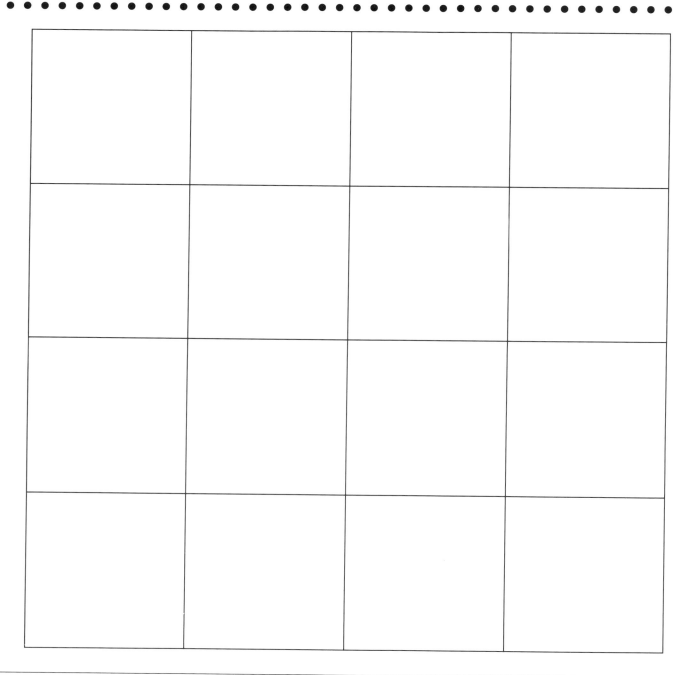

green bears

red bears

3

10

6

5

8

9

7

4

2

6

8

10

9

5

4

7

© LDA Compare Bears Maths Book 1

Paying with pennies

Aim

To use penny coins

Vocabulary

Penny, pence, coin, total, buy, cost, price

Materials

A box of 1-penny coins

Activity 1   Talking about shopping

Ask each child to take a large, medium and small bear. 'A large bear costs 3 pence. Put three pennies beside him.' Introduce the medium bear for 2 pence and the small bear for 1 penny. Encourage the children to talk about shopping and buying the bears before giving them the activity sheets.

ACTIVITY SHEET 57

Materials

1-penny coins

Encourage the children to put coins beside the bears at the top of the activity sheet. Match the bears to the stools, match the money to the bears.

ACTIVITY SHEET 58

Materials

1-penny coins

Children collect the penny coins that can be spent. They distribute the coins to the large, medium or small bear to see which bears they can buy.

ACTIVITY SHEET 59

Materials

1-penny coins

Ensure the children understand the vertical method of addition. Encourage them to collect the coins for each bear, count them and write the total in the box.

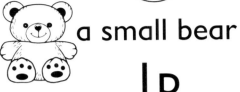 a small bear **1p**

 a medium bear **2p**

 a large bear **3p**

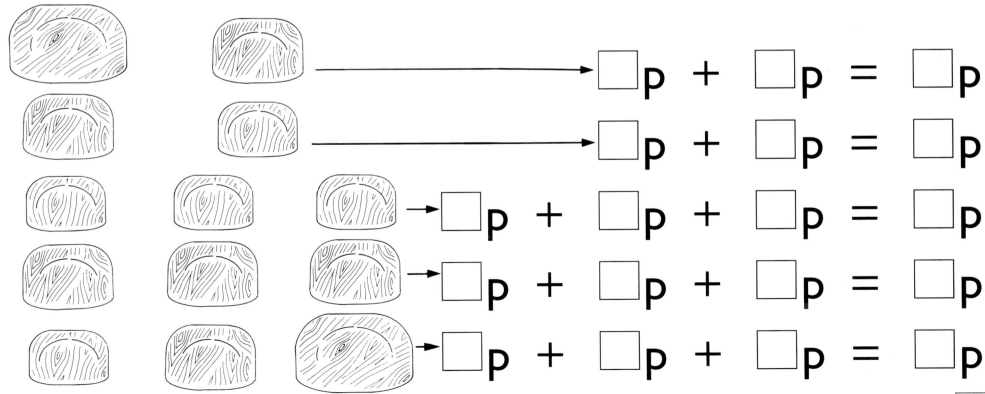

☐p + ☐p = ☐p

☐p + ☐p = ☐p

→ ☐p + ☐p + ☐p = ☐p

→ ☐p + ☐p + ☐p = ☐p

→ ☐p + ☐p + ☐p = ☐p

• •

a large bear

3p

a medium bear

2p

a small bear

1p

(1p) (1p) (1p)   (1p) (1p)   (1p)

4p   buys   1 large bear and 1 small bear

5p   buys _____

7p   buys _____

8p   buys _____

9p   buys _____

10p buys _____

85

© LDA Compare Bears Maths Book 1

 a large bear **3p**

 a medium bear **2p**

 a small bear **1p**

buy

1 large bear ☐ p
2 medium bears ☐ p
total ☐ p

2 large bears ☐ p
3 small bears ☐ p
total ☐ p

3 medium bears ☐ p
4 small bears ☐ p
total ☐ p

4 medium bears ☐ p
1 small bear ☐ p
total ☐ p

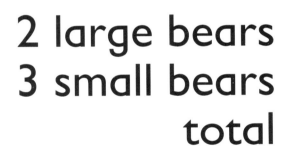

Probability

Aim

To discover how chance works

Vocabulary

Guess, probably, tick, first, second, third, totals, example

Materials

A bag

Activity 1 Line up the bears

Put out five yellow and five green medium bears. Emphasise the equal number. Match the bears one to one. Count in 2s. Put the bears in the bag. Ask a child to guess the colour before drawing out the first bear. Record the guess and the colour. Continue to guess before drawing out each bear. Line up the bears so that the children can see how many green and yellow bears remain in the bag. Encourage the children to talk about the results and the probability of guessing the right colour as the number in the bag decreases. 'If there are more yellow bears than green bears left in the bag, which colour will you probably draw?' Make a graph.

draw	guess	colour drawn	yes	no
1	y	y	√	
2	y	g		√
3	g	g	√	
4				

Activity 2 Put the bears back

Repeat the activity, but this time return the bears to the bag after each draw.
Encourage the children to talk about the change in their ideas about which colour will be drawn when all ten bears are always in the bag.

ACTIVITY SHEET 60

Materials

one red, three yellow and six green bears; a bag

Two children can work together sharing a bag but with separate sheets. Explain that the first line is an example. When the sheets are complete, compare the totals. Make a graph of the totals of the group.

There are 10 bears in the bag, 1 red, 3 yellow and 6 green. Guess which colour you will draw out first.
Put a tick for the colour you draw first. Put the bear back in the bag.
Guess which colour you will draw out second.

draw	guessed	red	yellow	green
example	red	✓		
1				
2				
3				
4				
5				
6				
7				
8				
9				
10				
	totals			

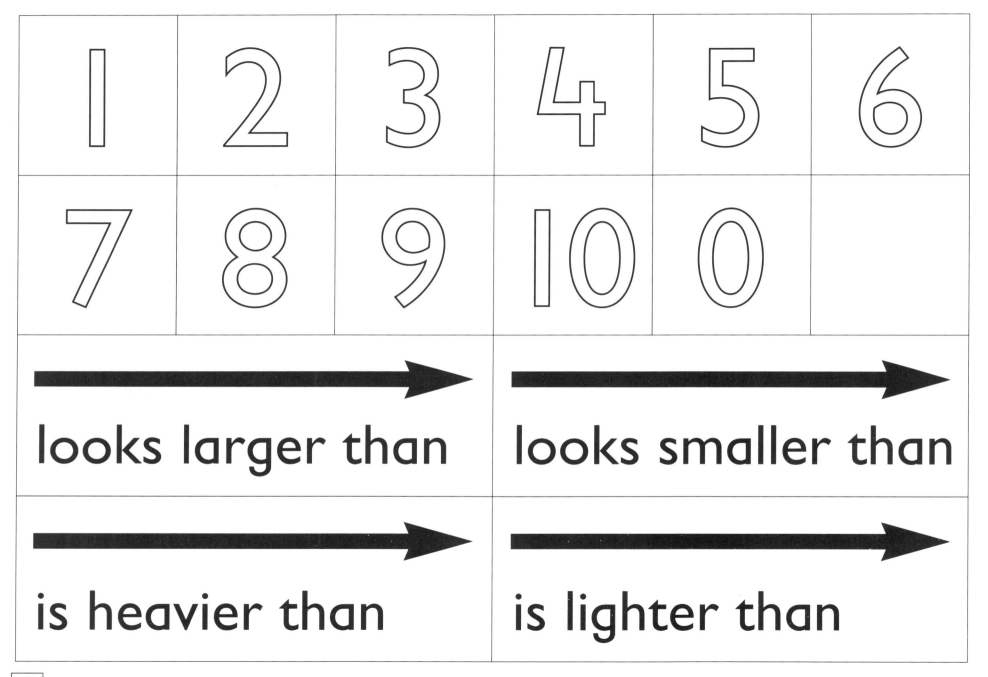

1 2 3 4 5 6

7 8 9 10 0

looks larger than

looks smaller than

is heavier than

is lighter than

heavy	heavier
heaviest	light
lighter	lightest

→

weighs the same as

smaller	smallest
middle-size	+
purple	medium
orange	=	−

red	blue
green	yellow
large	larger
largest	small

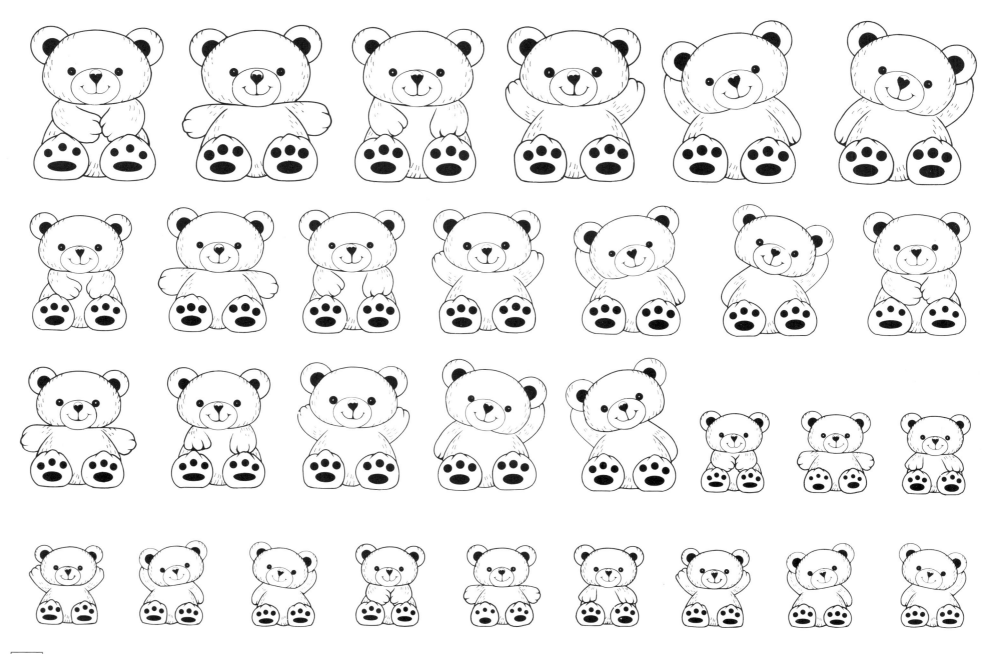